TAKING YOUR CHILD TO THE DOCTOR OR THE HOSPITAL

*Helpful suggestions and
practical tips
to make your child's visit
more comfortable*

PATRICIA WEINER, MS

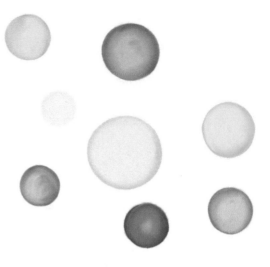

Publishing History

Taking Your Child to the Doctor or the Hospital: Helpful suggestions and practical tips to make your child's visit more comfortable
Copyright © 2013 by PATRICIA WEINER, MS
Illustrations copyright © 2013 by Wendy Borges

Library of Congress Cataloging in Publication Data U.S. Copyright Office in Washington D.C.
Number 1-1002837913
Patricia Weiner, MS

Includes contents. 1. Infants and Children-Healthcare - going to the doctor or hospital
2. Tips and suggestions for parents taking their children for well-child routine exams, immunizations or sick visits 3. Coping techniques for parents to use with their infants and children when they go to the doctor or hospital 4. When a child goes to the hospital
5. Suggested books for children and parents 6. References

**Originally published as a guide through a grant from THE SCHNURMACHER FOUNDATIONS by Patricia Weiner, MS, CCLS. ©1999-2001 Going to the Doctor, Dentist or Hospital: A helpful guide for parents to use with their children
Revised in 2013**

ISBN 978-0-578-131863 - Paperback

Printed in the United States of America

Professionals Praise Patty Weiner

"*Recognizing Patty as a passionate expert on educational advocacy, she understands the developmental needs of children and will help ease their fears and anxiety through the coping techniques used in her book. Patty's expertise, creativity and knowing young children so well make this book something all parents will want to have when they take their child to the doctor or the hospital.*"

-Richard Thompson, PhD
Dean of the School of Arts and Sciences, The College of New Rochelle

"*Patty Weiner was my graduate mentor at Bank Street College of Education and one of the main reasons that I am working in my dream job as an infant developmental specialist today. I was inspired by her work and the way she found possibilities and opportunities in the world of infants that are often missed by others. Patty is a wealth of knowledge with an immense amount of experience advocating for children and their families in healthcare settings. From the moment I met Patty I was amazed by her generosity of her time, energy, knowledge, and warmth. She works tirelessly and selflessly and she has helped and inspired so many. In her book she provides just the type of useful information and tools to make your child's experience more comfortable.*"

-Emily Lawton, MSEd.
Infant Developmental Specialist, Perinatal Follow-Up Clinic, IWK
Health Centre, Halifax, Nova Scotia

"*When You Take Your Child to the Doctor or the Hospital is a useful, practical book for all parents. Patty Weiner's sage advice works wonders for infants and young children receiving immunizations as well as for children undergoing procedures for medical conditions. This book is a recommended addition to every parent's bookshelf!*"

-Maggie Hoffman, Health Advocate

"*Patty Weiner is a leading child advocate who has great expertise and knowledge in all matters concerning the health of children and physical well being of children. This book is a must for all parents, it will be my new baby gift for all parents.*"

-Regina Skyer, Esq.

"*There are many books written to assist parents and caregivers taking their children to the doctor or hospital; however, this is one of the most accessible books that I have had the pleasure to read. Patty puts the parent/caregiver, in the driver's seat with simple but powerful suggestions supported by whimsical illustrations. I will be recommending this valuable book to my students, parents, friends and colleagues - and most certainly will add it to my personal library.*"

-Troy Pinkney-Ragsdale MA,CCLS
Director, Child Life Program, Bank Street College of Education

Dedication

To Children and Families Everywhere

And especially to my loving husband, Bobby,
who graciously supported my long hours of work and has always
admired the work I do;

Our wonderful sons Eric and Jonathan and their dear wives,
Nancy and Abby;

Our cherished grandchildren Julia, Danny, Emma and Rachel
"who are the icing on the cake!"

And the beloved memory of my parents Sylvia and Donald Lipps who
helped to teach me the importance of helping others.

Acknowledgements

I want to thank among many supportive colleagues and friends

Lu and Wendy Borges for their patience and expertise in making this book a reality.
Wendy Borges whose charming illustrations enhance this book.
Andrea Byer for her lovely photographs.
Rachel Gorman a wonderful publicist.

The professionals who reviewed this book: Lita Anglin, MSIS, James Fagin, MD, Susan Gottlieb, MD, Maggie Hoffman, Emily Lawton, MSEd., Joanne Loewy, DA, LCAT, MT-BC, Troy Pinkney-Ragsdale, MA, CCLS, Jennifer Rojas, MS, Abby Schor, Regina Skyer, Esq., Jon Snyder, Ed.D., and Richard Thompson, PhD.

The Child Life and Rainbow School staff at North Shore University Hospital (1986-1999) on Long Island, New York, whose devoted work with children and their families inspired me.

Additional resources are available online at:
www.pattyweinerconsults.com/pattysbookclub.html

Note: Throughout this book I use "she/her" to refer to infants, young children and healthcare providers of both the masculine and feminine gender.

Disclaimer: The purpose of this book is to give parents practical tips and easy techniques to help their children feel more comfortable during healthcare experiences. It is not intended to replace speaking to your child's doctor, nurse, or other healthcare professional about your child's discomfort or pain.

Introduction

As a long term healthcare provider and child life specialist, I recognize the need for parents/caregivers to be better prepared in helping their children through doctor and hospital visits. This concise and helpful book includes techniques and tips on how to help and advocate for your child.

When you bring your infant or child for a routine check up, the pediatrician checks to make sure your child is healthy. Some of the things that are checked include your child's height, weight, eyes, lungs, heart, and reflexes. Your child's pediatrician also takes her temperature, looks down her throat, checks her ears and hearing, presses on her tummy and checks her blood pressure. Sometimes your child will need a vaccination which is another name for a shot. It hurts a little, but vaccinations help protect your child from childhood diseases.

There will be times when your infant or child may need a blood test or another procedure that may cause discomfort. Use the techniques and tips in this book to help comfort and soothe your infant or child. It is important to feel comfortable with your pediatrician and ask her questions about your child's health and development.

Much of this book is about suggestions, tips, activities and techniques to help prepare you and your child for routine visits to the doctor or if your child has to go to the hospital. It is of equal importance to know how to advocate for your child and to partner with the doctors and the healthcare team so that your child receives the care she deserves.

If your child is hospitalized it is important to include the siblings in a developmentally appropriate way. If you have questions or want more information on different topics please visit pattyweinerconsults.com or email me at patty@pattyweinerconsults.com.

Good luck always,

Patricia Weiner

Advocacy

Knowing how and when to advocate for your child is an important skill to learn. You know your child best and can be your child's strongest support! This book includes many ideas to help your child feel more comfortable at the doctor's office or at the hospital.

Advocacy is defined as an any action that supports, speaks in favor of, recommends, or argues for a cause on behalf of others. In healthcare situations, we are supporting our children and acting on their behalf at a time when they need help in advocating for themselves.

Partnering with your doctor or healthcare team is very important. Think about your child's visit ahead of time and explain any concerns that you may have about your child's visit to the doctor. Call and speak to your child's doctor or other healthcare professional if you have specific questions and would like to be better prepared.

Many children have some type of special need; some children have more than one. It may be in the area of anxiety, emotional or behavioral regulation, learning disabilities, difficulty hearing, seeing, processing information, or difficulty staying focused. If your child has any need unique to her and you feel that she will need some accommodations when you bring her to the doctor or the hospital, feel free to contact me at (212) 828-3927 or email me at patty@pattyweinerconsults.com. I can give you some additional tips specific to your child's needs, make a home visit in Manhattan, speak to your child's pediatrician or give you the name of a supportive professional at the hospital that your child is visiting.

Advocating for your child, being prepared for healthcare visits and learning techniques to help comfort your child are all important skills to have.

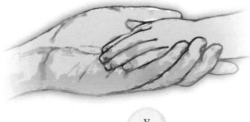

Contents

Contents

How to Use This Book

In this simple and concise book parents are given practical tips and easy suggestions along with easy to teach coping techniques to use when their child is going to the doctor or needs to go to the hospital.

This book is for parents to use with their children in order to:

- help them understand why doctor's visits are important.
- help children learn about going to the hospital for out-patient medical procedures or hospital admissions.
- give parents practical tips and easy suggestions to help comfort their child during healthcare experiences.
- teach children coping techniques to use at the doctor or hospital, including Preparation and Medical Play, Comforting Positions, Positive Reinforcement, Distraction, Guided Imagery, Deep Breathing, Positive Self-Talk, and Relaxation, to help children during healthcare experiences.
- learn activities to do with and discussions to have with your child before and after you go to the doctor or the hospital.

If your child has a special need and would benefit from professional advocacy (page v), contact me at (212) 828-3927 or email me at patty@pattyweinerconsults.com.

About Child Life

From 1922- 1949, pediatric play programs developed in North America for children in the hospital. In 1955, "Emma Plank, a child development specialist and pioneer in the field of Child Life was asked by Dr. Fred Robbins (Nobel Laureate) to create a program to address the social, emotional and educational needs of hospitalized children at Cleveland City Hospital. Emma Plank served as the director for the Child Life and Education Division until 1972" [1].

Since the 1970's to date, over 400 Child Life Programs have been established in North America and several around the world. The field of Child Life has grown and expanded with the focus on the psychosocial and developmental needs of children. Some of the services child life specialists provide today are: preparing children for medical procedures, teaching coping strategies to help reduce anxiety and stress, providing developmentally appropriate play, as well as medical and therapeutic play, and offering many activities that emphasize fun.

Child life specialists also provide family support and encourage family involvement. The child's family is the center of her world. Family centered care is a critical link to the well-being and the care of children. It is important that parents and health-care professionals work together to form a partnership to enhance every child's care.

When your child is hospitalized you will receive an Admissions Booklet welcoming you to the hospital. It will have information that explains all the various departments and services, people and numbers to call at the hospital. If you don't receive one then ask about what services are available at the hospital.

[1] www.childlife.org/The%20Child%20Life%20Profession/timeline.cfm

Child Life now includes providing programming in many other areas of the hospital such as in the outpatient departments, surgical and intensive care units, emergency departments, radiology, operating rooms, pediatrician's offices and with a growing presence in neonatal intensive care units.

Most hospitals have a Family Resource Center. It is a place where parents or caregivers gather more information about their child's condition, parents/caregivers can stay in touch with their child's doctors and other healthcare providers without having to talk in front of their child, call their office or friends to keep them informed. Parents can find out about activities for adults, have tea or coffee and have a place to chat with other parents or friends. In addition to books in the Family Resource Center there are computers and printers to help families access information.

School in the hospital is offered if a child is in kindergarten–12th grade or receiving special education services. The hospital arranges for a child or youth to receive **academic** education based or her length of stay and condition in accordance with law and regulation of each state and school district. Most hospitals in the United States offer school services. School in the hospital varies in each setting.

Ask the child life specialist, social worker or hospital teacher about this service. School promotes normalcy and keeps students up with their school work.

Child Life services are also being offered in **"non-traditional" and "alternative settings" beyond the hospital** such as special needs camps, early intervention services, non-profit organizations and private practices where child life specialists act as consultants providing either education, educational advocacy or counseling for children and their families surrounding many issues related to the child's illness.

Visits to the doctor or hospital stays are unfamiliar, frightening and sometimes painful. Child life specialists work with members of the healthcare team to make each child's experience more comfortable and less stressful. The techniques in this book are used by Child Life staff to help soothe a child's fears and, in many cases, speed recovery.

Sometimes a child life specialist is not available. It is important that parents know how to advocate for their child and know some of the suggestions and tips, including techniques to help *comfort, calm,* and *soothe* their child.

If your child is being admitted to the hospital or having surgery, either contact the doctor or call the Child Life Department at the hospital and ask if there is a 'pre-admission' or a 'pre-operative program' that they offer depending on your needs.

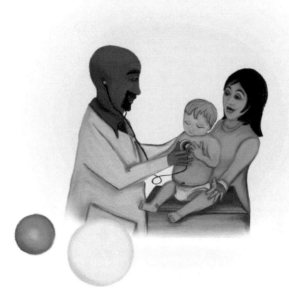

Tips and Suggestions for Parents

For All Infants and Children

- Prepare yourself for your child's visit. If you feel at ease, your child is able to sense that and react in the same way.

- Prepare a written list of questions that you want to ask the doctor. If your child isn't feeling well, it is important to include details of your child's symptoms and any concerns you might have.

- A great way for toddlers and preschoolers to prepare for going to the doctor is to *play* doctor. Let your child use a toy doctor's kit and give her a doll or stuffed toy so she can give her doll a checkup. She can check her doll's heart, reflexes, ears, eyes, weigh her, measure her, and feel her tummy. Toy doctor's kits come with a play stethoscope, otoscope, reflex hammer, and a pretend syringe for shots/injections. You can use materials found in your house; band-aids, alcohol (to show how cold an alcohol wipe is), and gauze pads. It's fun and educational for your child to 'play doctor'.

- Speak to your child's physician about types of pain relief before your first visit. You might want to discuss pain medicine for immunizations, injections or other painful medical procedures. Sometimes local anesthetics that you can apply at home prior to or following a procedure are recommended. Some pediatricians use other methods for pain relief.

- Stay with your infant or young child during the doctor's office visit whenever possible. Separation is one of the most difficult experiences for a young child. A parent's presence is comforting and healing.

- It's important to use comforting positions for your infant or child. Holding infants or having them sit on your lap gives them a sense of security, control, and comfort.

- Take a familiar toy, teddy or blanket to the doctor's office. It may help comfort your infant or child.

- Children find comfort in routine and discipline. It is a good idea to keep consistent.

- Do something fun when the visit is done.

Helping Your Baby to be Soothed and Comforted

- Babies and young children love to be held or sit in a comforting position on their mom or dad's lap.

- As the children get older they may want one of their parents to hold their hand.

- Babies love to suck and it is soothing to them - breast or bottle feed, help them find their fingers or pacifier.

- Infants love movement, it soothes them. Hold, walk, sway, or rock with your baby.

- Stroke your infants face - infants love gentle touch.

- Sing or hum softly to your baby. Infants enjoy music and familiar voices.

- Bottle or breast feed after appointment or procedure is completed.

- Bring your child's favorite snack and offer it to her after the appointment or procedure.

For Children:

- Use simple, concrete language. Be honest. Give information to your child that will help prepare her for a visit to the doctor, hospital or for a specific procedure. What will she see, hear, smell and have to do (i.e., weight, height, hold still, answer doctor's questions)?

- Help your child express her feelings and/or fears and prepare her through play. Playing doctor is one way of helping your toddler or preschooler prior to your visit.

- Reading some of the books listed in the Suggested Readings page to your child before you go to the doctor or hospital will help prepare her for healthcare experiences. Call your local library or contact the hospital's Child Life Department for additional age-appropriate books and toys for your child.

- Reassure your child. Make sure your child knows going to the doctor or hospital is not a punishment and is not necessarily a place where she will feel pain. Sometimes your child will need immunizations or medicines given by injection or a blood test to find out how her body is working. Reassure your child that her body keeps making more blood all the time.

- Give your child choices when possible. Choices give your child a sense of control. Your child can choose which arm to use for an injection, or whether or not to watch a procedure. She can pick out her favorite Band-aid or sticker! Having choices will help her to get through the procedure. Try not to make promises you can't keep.

- Listen to your child's concern. It is okay to ask questions, to want to watch the procedure, cry and talk about her feelings. Crying is a release for tension, anger and hurt.

- Use the comforting positions and other coping techniques discussed in the book. Use the photographs for distraction or guided imagery. Bring bubbles, rattles or other distraction toys that your child likes.

- Bring crayons for drawing. Exam table paper makes a great canvas.

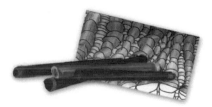

- Bring your child's favorite music and earphones with you or sing a familiar song to your child. Music is a wonderful way to support and soothe your child.

- Praise your child and bring small rewards with you for positive reinforcement. Encourage her during the procedure.

FOUR
Techniques

1. Preparation and Medical Play

2. Comforting Positions

3. Positive Reinforcement

4. Distraction

5. Deep Breathing

6. Guided Imagery

7. Positive Self-Talk

8. Relaxation

9. Summary

Explore activities you can do with your child on page 16.

1. Preparation and Medical Play *(15 months through all ages)*

Children benefit by being prepared briefly for visits to the doctor or hospital. Consider preparing toddlers and preschoolers **one day ahead** of their visit or on the way to the doctor. School age children sometimes are best prepared one day prior to their visit. Adolescents should be informed sooner especially if they are going to the hospital. Parents are the best judge of when to tell their children about doctor or hospital visits.

If your child is going to the hospital, more preparation is usually needed. Call the director of the Child Life Program at the hospital and ask about any "pre-admission" or "pre-operative" programs.

The following are some suggestions to help prepare your child:

- Prepare yourself first. Ask your child's doctor for more specific information about the procedure.

- You know your child best of all. Help your child get ready by talking with her.

- Choose a quiet time to talk to your child. Using a calm and comforting voice will help your child to be relaxed.

- Explain the reason for the visit or procedure.

- Offer your child honest, sensitive and developmentally appropriate information that she can understand.

- Prepare your child for what will happen. Use 'hands on materials' for young children.

- Ask your child what might "help" during the procedure or hospital visit.

- Read books with your child about going to the doctor or hospital.

- Role-play with a doll or stuffed toy to help prepare your child. Your child can pretend the doll or stuffed toy is going to the doctor and can give the doll a check up, listen to its heart or even give the doll an injection. Playing doctor is a great way to prepare and teach your child about medical sounds, smells and sights. Play gives children a sense of control and a way to work out and understand their feelings.

- Use a doll or stuffed toy to provide a safe way to talk to your child about her feelings and what will occur.

- Ask your child if she wants to bring the doll or toy to the doctor or hospital.

If your child goes to the hospital, she will feel better learning about the hospital and getting ready for the new experiences. The "clingy" infant arrives around 10 months of age, and parents know when they see it. Suddenly, leaving the child's line of sight causes the little one great distress - thanks in part to the child's undeveloped sense of time and lack of experience with a parent's absence. **Sometimes during stressful situations, separation from parents is more difficult and distress lasts for a longer time. Don't leave your child without telling her that you will be back soon.**

Fortunately, separation anxiety passes with time. It's a normal stage of development for most children, usually ending by the last half of the second year. As the toddler learns that parents keep coming back after they leave, the fear subsides and the child's confidence builds. It's getting from here to there that can make for some trying moments, and often some tender ones, as well.

As a child grows, those fears change. The fears of body changes, pain, appearance and privacy deepen as the child gets older. Many hospitals offer a special program with hands-on activities for children, where they can see and explore real medical equipment. Ask your child's doctor for this information. Pre-admission and pre-operative programs are usually offered by the Child Life department at your hospital or through the Department of Pediatrics. For a hospital visit, you can pack some special things to have from home. Most children pack a few favorite things like pajamas, books, games or a special toy. Some children like to bring pictures from home or their own blanket or pillow.

Some tests and procedures may hurt in the hospital. Use the techniques in this book to help your child during difficult times. Use the hospital check list included in this book to help you get ready for a hospital stay. Ask to speak to a child life specialist or a nurse. She will help your child during her hospitalization.

2. Comforting Positions *(Infancy and up)*

You are the best source of comfort for your child! Hold your infant or young child. Have your infant/child sit on your lap (chest to chest, sideways, or back to chest). This will help your child stay calm, feel in control and be comforted. You can practice hugging! Holding your infant in an upright position or having your child sit on your lap will help her relax. When a child lies on her back she feels vulnerable. Physical touch provides security and warmth. Touching includes stroking, swaddling, holding, rocking and cuddling.

Once infants learn to sit up, they are so proud of this milestone that the act of making an infant or child lie down may result in her crying or her struggling to get up.

School-age children sometimes like to hold their parent's hand and teenagers should be given the choice of what they want to do.

You can see photos of different comforting positions on my page: www.pattyweinerconsults.com/pattysbookclub

3. Positive Reinforcement *(Six months and up)*

Lavish your child with praise! Praise your child for helping and staying still. Praise your child for having finished the procedure even if she cries. Remember that crying is a way of coping for some children. Bring small rewards such as stickers and other treats.

4. Distraction *(Six months and up)*

If your child wants to watch the procedure let her! If not, help your child focus on something other than the procedure. Read a pop-up book or storybook; sing a song; focus on a soothing, diversional object; look at photographs and talk to your child about them; blow on a pinwheel; recite familiar nursery rhymes; blow bubbles; practice counting or saying the alphabet. Older children may enjoy playing with electronic games, a computer tablet or listening to music with earphones. Before the visit, help your child create a list of things she would like to use as a distraction. Bring some toys with you.

5. Deep Breathing *(School-age and up)*

Deep breathing will help your child to relax and slow her heart rate. Help your child get into a comfortable position. Tell your child to breathe in deeply through her nose, count to three and blow out through her mouth. Encourage your child throughout the procedure. Breathe with your child and breathe slowly! Use explanations your child will understand when explaining the breathing (for example, take a deep breath in like you are smelling flowers, count to three, and blow out slowly as if you were blowing out lots of birthday candles). Use a pinwheel, breathe in, count to three and then blow on the pinwheel. Pinwheels are fun to watch and help your child relax. Blowing bubbles always helps with deep breathing.

6. Guided Imagery *(School-age and up)*

Help your child see a picture in her mind of something or someone that she likes. Children do not have to close their eyes (many are afraid of "sneak attacks"), but it is helpful. Combine imagery with deep breathing. In a soothing voice, tell your child a story. Some things children like to imagine are stories of stars, rainbows, snowflakes, butterflies, animals, flowers, the beach or their favorite places. You could place your child on a magic carpet that flies over rivers, mountains and lakes and help her to visualize this in her mind.

7. Positive Self-Talk *(Preschool and up)*

This technique is used prior to a painful procedure and should be ongoing. Encourage your child to replace negative thoughts with positive ones. This technique relies on a self-fulfilling prophecy. For example, help your child to stop thoughts like, "I can't do this" or "This is going to hurt". Help her to replace negative thoughts with comments like, "This might hurt a little, but I will feel better soon" or "I know I can do it!". Tell your child what a good job she is doing. Support and encouragement during the procedure will help your child feel more comfortable.

8. Relaxation *(School-age and up)*

Help your child to relax her body so that she will feel more comfortable. Have her lie down and get comfy. Now, have her close her eyes and begin to relax her body as you talk. Ask her to wiggle her toes and feet and then let them relax. Next have your child squeeze her eyes tight and then let them relax. Tell your child to squeeze her whole body tight and let it relax and be floppy like a rag doll. This is fun to do and helps her learn to relax. When you visit the doctor, your child can pretend to be floppy in a sitting position. Your child can also squeeze and release a tension ball.

9. Summary of Coping Techniques and Materials By Age

Infants

Parental Presence	*Distractions* (6 months +), i.e.:
Comforting Positions	spinning toy, pinwheel, rattle
Rapid Rocking and Patting	
Sucking	
Singing	
Music	

Toddlers

Parental Presence	*Distractions*, i.e.: photographs,
Comforting Positions	pop-up book, pinwheel, magic wand,
Music	spinning toy, bubble blowing
Rocking	
Singing	

Preschoolers

Parental Presence	*Distractions*, i.e.: pop-up book,
Comforting Positions	magic wand, use photograph,
Singing	spinning toy, bubble blowing
Music	
	Imagery, i.e.: favorite story or favorite place
	Deep breathing, i.e.: Breathe in, count to three and pretend to blow out candles on a birthday cake, or blow on a pinwheel

School Age

Parental Presence (*as needed*)	***Distractions***, i.e.: books, spinning toy, pinwheel, magic wand or an iPad (supervised by a child life specialist or parent), bubble blowing
Singing	
Music	

Relaxation i.e.: rag doll, tension ball

Imagery, i.e.: favorite place or favorite story

Deep breathing, i.e.: Breathe in, count to three and pretend to blow out candles on a birthday cake, or blow on a pinwheel

- If your child is hospitalized, reach out to the Child Life Department.

FIVE
Activities

Explore the activities on the following pages with your child.

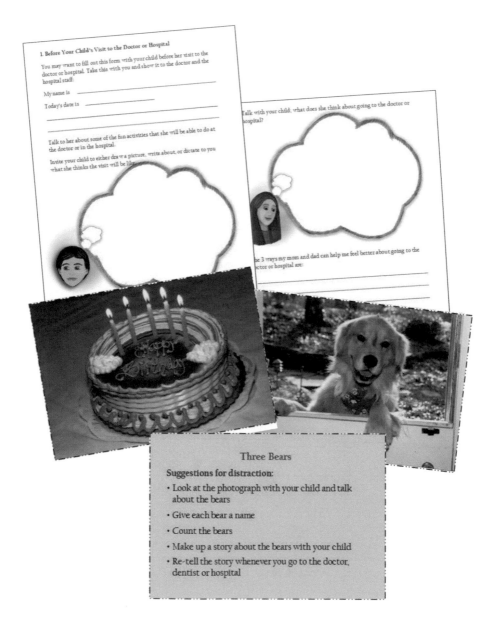

1. Before Your Child's Visit to the Doctor or Hospital

You may want to fill out this form with your child before her visit to the doctor or hospital. Take this with you and show it to the doctor and the hospital staff:

My name is _____

Today's date is _____

_____

Talk to her about some of the fun activities that she will be able to do at the doctor or in the hospital.

Invite your child to either draw a picture, write about, or dictate to you what she thinks the visit will be like.

Talk with your child; what does she think about going to the doctor or hospital?

3 ways my mom and dad can help me feel better about going to the doctor or hospital are:

Three Bears

Suggestions for distraction:

• Look at the photograph with your child and talk about the bears

• Give each bear a name

• Count the bears

• Make up a story about the bears with your child

• Re-tell the story whenever you go to the doctor, dentist or hospital

1. Before Your Child's Visit to the Doctor or Hospital

You may want to fill out this form with your child before her visit to the doctor or hospital. Take this with you and show it to the doctor and the hospital staff:

My name is _____

Today's date is _____

I am going to the doctor or hospital for:

_____

_____

_____

Talk to her about some of the fun activities that she will be able to do at the doctor or in the hospital.

Invite your child to either draw a picture, write about, or dictate to you what she thinks the visit will be like:

17

Talk with your child; what does she think about going to the doctor or hospital?

The 3 ways my mom and dad can help me feel better about going to the doctor or hospital are:

1 _____

2 _____

3 _____

2. Cards To Take With You

Cut out the following cards to take with you to the doctor's office or the hospital to use as relaxation techniques. *An online version can be seen at www.pattyweinerconsults.com/pattysbookclub.html*

Three Bears

Suggestions for distraction:

- Look at the photograph with your child and talk about the bears

- Give each bear a name

- Count the bears

- Make up a story about the bears with your child

- Re-tell the story whenever you go to the doctor, dentist or hospital

Birthday Cake

Suggestions for deep breathing:

- Ask your child to take a deep breath in through her nose (like she's smelling flowers)

- Then count to three

- Look at the photograph of the birthday cake

- Ask your child to blow out slowly like she is blowing out the candles on the birthday cake.

- Practice doing this along with your child.

Birdhouses

Suggestions for distraction:

- Look at the photograph with your child and talk about the birdhouses

- Count the birdhouses

- Look for and describe the details on the birdhouses

- Make up a story with your child about the birdhouses

Dog Looking Through Window

Suggestions for distraction:

- Look at the photograph of the dog with your child and talk about the dog

- Does the dog look friendly?

- Do you think the dog is small?

- What kind of dog do you think it is? *(golden retriever)*

- Do you have or want a dog or pet? *(optional question)*

SIX

Questions To Ask The Doctor, If Your Child Requires Hospitalization

Gather information from your child's doctor so that you and your child will know what to expect. Some helpful questions to ask may include:

- What will happen at the hospital?

- How long will my child be in the hospital?

- Could the doctor put me in touch with the hospital's Child Life department before I go to the hospital? Call and speak to a child life specialist before admitted to the hospital.

- Will I be able to stay overnight in my child's room with her?

- Will I be able to stay with my child during anesthesia induction before the surgery?

- Will I be able to be with my child in the recovery room after the surgery?

- What can be done to relieve her discomfort or pain?

- What will my child be able to do while in the hospital?

- Will there be school in the hospital?

- Will she experience any physical changes? What will they be?

- Who will help us plan to go home?

- Will she be able to attend school when she comes home? If she can't, who in the hospital will help us set up home instruction and help her to receive home instruction or any special services that she may have?

SEVEN

Getting Ready to Go to the Hospital

Ask your child what she may want to have with her in the hospital. Make a checklist with her and talk about what to expect at the hospital. Some things she might want to bring with her are:

- Books or magazines

- A favorite stuffed toy

- A favorite pillow or blanket

- Pictures of her family or pet

- Some pens, pencils and a pad of paper

- A watch or clock (depending on her age)

- A favorite game

- A toothbrush, toothpaste, a cup and other things from home

EIGHT

After Your Visit to the Doctor or Hospital

- After your visit to the doctor or hospital, talk to your child about how she felt.

- Talk about any discomfort your child might have had.

- Play doctor and allow your child to care for her teddy bear or stuffed toy. Playing doctor after a child is finished with an exam or hospitalization helps her process what happened and how she felt.

- It is a good idea to discuss with your child ways that will make going to the doctor or to the hospital easier the next time. It is easier if you write a list together and save it.

NINE

Suggested Reading for Children

Books about healthcare experiences should present helpful information for children in a truthful and encouraging manner. Books such as these help familiarize children with medical personnel and procedures, and serve to minimize their anxieties about the experience. *Please note that this list is not exclusive and that you may have your own favorites.*

Books about going to the doctor for young children

Berenstain, Stan and Jan Berenstain. *The Berenstain Bears Go to The Doctor.* New York, New York: Random House Inc., 1981.

Brazelton, T. Berry, *Going to the Doctor.* Reading, Mass.: Addison-Welsey/ Lawrence, 1987.

Civardi, Anne, and Stephen Cartwright. *Going to the Doctor.* London, England: Usborne Publishing Ltd., 1988, 1999.

Markoff, Heifi. *What to Expect When You Go to the Doctor.* Harper Collins Publisher, 2000.

Zoehfeld, K.W. *Pooh Plays Doctor,* 1999. Using Christopher Robin's doctor kit, Pooh finds out about reflexes, heartbeats, blood pressure, and shots. Pooh is not sick but when told he has to go to the doctor, says he starts to feel sick. Basic and good for young children.

Books about going to the hospital for young children

Bemelman, Ludwig. *Madeline.* New York: Puffin, 1977.

Civardi, Anne, and Stephen Cartwright. *Going to the Hospital.* London, England: Usborne Publishing Ltd., 1987, 1992.

Hautzig, Deborah. *A Visit to the Sesame Street Hospital.* Westminister, Maryland: Random House, 1985.

Jennings, S. *Franklin Goes to the Hospital.* Kids Can Press LTD, Jan. 1, 2000.

Rey, Margaret and H.A. *Curious George Goes to the Hospital.* Houghton Mifflin Co., 1966.

Rogers, Fred. *Going to the Hospital*. Topeka, Kansas: Econo-Clad Book, 1999.

Wood, J.R., *What Will I See? And Who are Those People Wearing Funny Clothes?* Author House, 2009.

Books about going to the hospital for older children

Hogan, P. and K. *The Hospital Scares Me*. Raintree Publications, 1980.

Howe, Jane. *The Hospital Book*. New York: Crown, 1991.

Richter, E. *The Teenage Hospital Experience: You Can Handle It!* New York: Coward, McCann and Geoghegan, 1982.

Stein, Sara Bonnet. *A Hospital Story: An Open Family Book for Parents and Children Together*. New York: Walker and Company, 1983.

Suggested Reading for Parents

Books about child development, parenting, child life, child psychology, childhood pain, hospitalization and coping techniques:

Achterberg, Jeanne. *Imagery in Healing*. Boston, Mass.: New Science Library, 1985.

Bowlby, John. *Attachment and Loss*. 3 vols. New York: Basic B books, 1969-1980.

Boston Children's Hospital. *The New Child Health Encyclopedia: The Complete Guide for Parents*. New York: Delacorte Press/ Lawrence, 1987.

Brazelton, T. Berry: *Touchpoints*. Reading, Mass.: Perseus Books, 1992.
_____. *To Listen to a Child*. Reading, Mass.: AddisonWesley/Lawrence, 1984.
_____. *Working and Caring*, Reading. Mass.: AddisonWesley/Lawrence, 1985.

Cohen, Michel. *The New Basics. A-Z Baby &Child Care for the Modern Parent*. HarperCollins Publishers, 2004.

Epstein, Gerald. *Healing Visualizations: Creative Health Through Imagery*. New York. Bantam Books, 1989.

Erickson, Erik. *Childhood and Society*. New York: Norton, 1950.

Fraiberg, Selma M. *The Magic Years*. New York: Scribner's, 1959.

Galinsky, Ellen. *The Six Stages of Parenthood*. Reading, Mass.: Addison-Wesley/Lawrence, 1987.

Krieger, Doris. *Accepting Your Power to Heal: The Practice of Therapeutic Touch*. Santa Fe, NM: Bear and Co., 1993.

Kutter, Leora. *A Child in Pain, How to Help What to Do*. Hartley and Marks Publishers Inc., 1966.

Leach, Penelope. *Babyhood*. New York: Knopf, 1976.
_____. *Your Baby and Child*, 1977, 1997.

Loewy, J.V., MacGregor, B., Richards, K., and Rodriguez, J. *Music Therapy and Pediatric Pain*. Cherry Hill, NJ: Jeffrey Books, 1997.

McGrath, P., *Pain in Children: Nature, Assessment and Treatment*. New York: Guilford Press, 1990.

Murkoff, Heidi. *What to Expect the First Year*. HarperCollins Publishers, 2012.

Murdock, M. *Spinning Inwards*. Boston, Mass.: Shambhala Publications, Inc., 1987.

Petrillo, Madeline, and Sirgay Sanger. *Emotional Care of Hospitalized Children*. Philadelphia, Pennsylvania: J.B. Lippincott Company, 1980.

Sears, William., Sears, Martha. *The Baby Book: Everything You Need to Know About Your Baby from Birth to Age Two*. Little, Brown and Company, 2003.

Thompson RH, Stanford G. *Child Life in Hospitals: Theory and Practice*. Springfield, IL: Charles C Thomas, 1981.

Anthology of Focus is available to purchase on Child Life Council's site. It includes an article on 'Coping Kits and Distraction Techniques' by Simone Blaine in the June 1999 bulletin. It is in included in the Anthology of Focus; as well as other newsletters from June 1999 through fall 2009.

References and Resources

Books and Journal Articles

American Academy of Pediatrics Child Life Council and Committee on Hospital Care, Wilson, J.M. (2006). Child life services. *Pediatrics,* 118 (4), 1757-63.

Blaine, Simone. (1999). Coping kits and distraction techniques. *Child Life Focus,* 1 (1).

Child Life Council (2009). Anthology of *Child Life Focus* (1999-2009): Child Life Council Bulletin Newsletter.

Gaynard L., Wolfer J., Goldberger J., Thompson R., Redburn L., Laidley L. (1998). *Psychosocial Care of Children in Hospitals: A Clinical Practice Manual.* Rockville, MD: Child Life Council.

Hicks, M. (2008). *Child Life Beyond the Hospital.* Child Life Council.

Loewy, J. (1999). Music Therapy Significant Helper in Healing, Soothing children. *AAP News* 15 (12), 29-32.

Meyer, D.J., Vadasy, P.F. (2008). *Sibshops: Workshops for Siblings of Children with Special Needs, Revised Edition.* Brookes Publishing.

Plank, E.N. (1959). *Working With Children in Hospitals, A Guide for the Professional Team.* London, England: Tavistock Publications.

Roberts, M.C., Maieron, M.J., Collier, J. (1988). *Directory of Psychosocial Policies and Programs.* Bethesda, MD: Association for the Care of Children's Health.

Stephens, B.K., Barkey, M.E., Hall, H.R. (1999). Techniques to comfort children during stressful procedures. *Advances in Mind-Body Medicine.* Pages 15, 49-60.

Thompson, R., (Ed.). (2009). *The Handbook of Child Life: A Guide for Pediatric Psychosocial Care.* Springfield, IL: Charles C. Thomas.

Thompson, R.H., Stanford, G. (1981). *Child Life in Hospitals: Theory and Practice.* Springfield, IL: Charles C. Thomas.

Website Articles

Child Life Council, Inc. (2014). Resources for Caregivers. *Childlife.org* Retrieved February 9, 2014, from http://www.childlife.org/Resource%20Library/ResourcesforCaregivers.cfm

Child Life Council, Inc. (2014). Power to the Parents Tip Sheet. *Childlife.org* Retrieved February 9, 2014, from http://www.childlife.org/files/PowerParentsTipSheet.pdf

Nemours Foundation. Doctor visits. *KidsHealth.org* Retrieved February 9, 2014 from www.kidshealth.org/parent/system/doctor/dr_visits.html#cat173

PBS Parents. Talking With Kids about Health: Going to the Doctor & Dentist – Before You Go and When You're There. *PBS.org* Retrieved February 9, 2014 from www.pbs.org/parents/talkingwithkids/health/doctor.html

Weiner, P. (2001). Going to the Doctor, Dentist or Hospital: A Helpful Guide for Parents to Use with Their Children. *PattyWeinerConsults.com.* Retrieved February 9, 2014 from http://www.pattyweinerconsults.com/resources/goingtothedoctor.pdf

All links are available at Patty's book club page:
www.pattyweinerconsults.com/pattysbookclub.html

About Patricia Weiner

Patricia Weiner is a mother and grandmother whose career spans over thirty-five years as a child life specialist and educator. With an MS in Special Education, she served as the Director of Child Life and Education Services at North Shore-Long Island Jewish Medical Center. She was the founding Director of the Master's Degree program in Child Life at Bank Street College of Education in New York.

Patty is presently an educational and child life consultant practicing in Manhattan; an educational consultant for The Making Headway Foundation, a not-for-profit organization dedicated to children with brain and spinal cord tumors and their families; a member of the On-Going Care Team who provide post hospitalization care for these children and their families; and, a graduate school student mentor in the Child Life program at Bank Street College.

She is an expert blog contributor for Mommybites, which provides parenting resources, support and education, Patty's work has been presented in a variety of professional forums and publications.

For additional information about the author, go to:
www.pattyweinerconsults.com or
email her at patty@pattyweinerconsults.com

Made in the USA
Charleston, SC
18 March 2014